Recorder Duets
from the Beginning

CW00430022

John Pitts

Duet playing brings extra pleasure to all involved, and with it an incentive to learn new notes and rhythms in order to succeed. A simultaneous development of listening skills and concentration is also required for successful ensemble playing.

Recorder Duets from the Beginning Books 1, 2 and 3 provide a wide range of repertoire to encourage duet playing by descant recorder players, both accompanied and unaccompanied. All the items are carefully graded, both in range of notes (pitches) included and in the level of difficulty. It is expected that players using Book 1 will have already reached the end of *Recorder from the Beginning Book 1*, in the author's widely popular teaching scheme.

Early pieces have matching rhythms in both parts, making it easier for the players to keep in time together. Then some independence of parts is gradually introduced, including the use of imitation and counting of rests, plus more sophisticated rhythms.

The Pupil's Books include guitar chord symbols, and the Latin American items have suggestions for use of percussion instruments. The Teacher's Books include piano accompaniments for all the duets as well as the Latin American percussion parts.

In keeping with the 'repertoire' nature of the books, only a minimum of teaching help or explanation is given. Where more help is required it is best to refer to the appropriate pages of the teaching scheme *Recorder from the Beginning*.

Chester Music Limited
(A division of Music Sales Limited)
8/9 Frith Street, London W1V 5TZ

Contents

Way Down South

Les Bouffons French

Irish Lullaby

Chandos Fanfare   Pitts

Ode To Joy Beethoven

Allegro moderato

Banks of the Ohio American

Fais Dodo   French Lullaby

10

Now All the Forests　　German

Pokare Kare   Maori Song

For introduction use last
4 bars of piano accompaniment

Kaluszin Mazurka   Pitts

Tango Chacabuco   Pitts

The Pupil's Book includes the following suggestion for a rhythm ostinato accompaniment. This will add flavour to the piece, whether or not the piano is used.

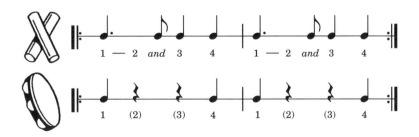

Michael, Row the Boat Ashore

Gavotte   Handel

17

Soracaba Beguine   Pitts

Beguine percussion accompaniment:
Play the first rhythm on claves.

The second rhythm can be played on maracas. A good idea is for the second player to count out loud each beat, playing the maracas in between.

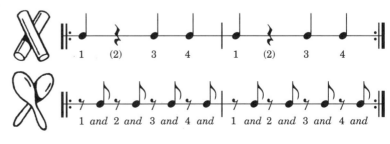

Rigaudon Chédeville

Accompaniment: here is an optional rhythm ostinato to add to the duet, whether or not the piano is used. It is best to use a **tambour.** This has a vellum head like a tambourine, but no jingles. They come in different sizes and the larger ones can be tuned. You can vary the sound of all tambours by using different kinds of beaters — or just use your fingers to tap out the rhythm. Make sure you bounce your hand straight off after tapping, so the sound is not muffled.

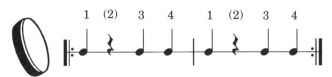

Ye Banks and Braes   Scottish

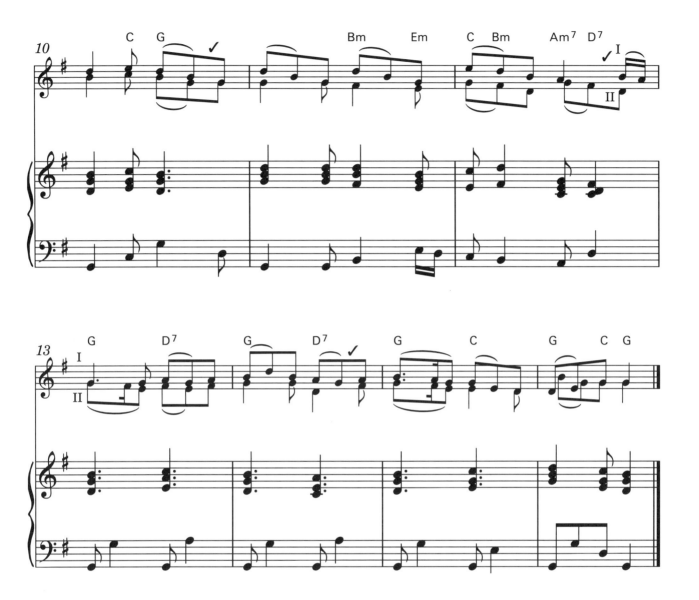

The words to this song are by Robert Burns (1759-96), the Scottish poet and songwriter. The tune was originally called 'The Caledonian Hunt's Delight' and was published in 1788. Burns wrote his words to fit the tune and published them in 1792, popularising the tune under its new title. The song is still well known today.

Like many Scottish folksongs, the tune uses the restricted range of notes called the **pentatonic scale.** For the sake of variety, the 2nd recorder part and piano accompaniment given here use the full major scale and are not restricted to the pentatonic scale.

Boogie Blues   Pitts

Tango La Pampa   Pitts

The Pupil's Book suggests making use of the same percussion accompaniment we used for Tango Chacabuco on page 15.

Here are the same rhythm ostinatos, but for variety you could swop the instrumentation to maracas and claves.

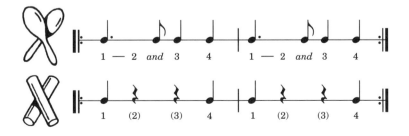

The Pearly Adriatic   Yugoslavian

Scarborough Fair

31

Menuetto   W.A. Mozart

Panis Angelicus   César Frank

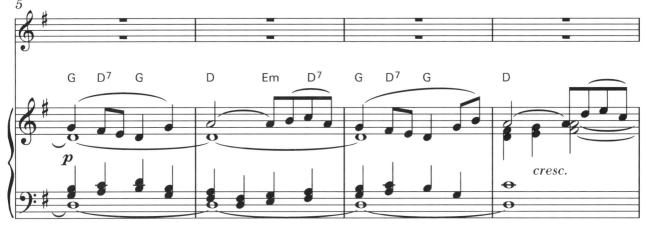

11/02 (45853)